DOMENICO SCARLATTI
(1685-1757)
TEN SONATAS
Selected and Edited by Keith Snell

CONTENTS

For supplementary study, a recording is available on compact disc of the sonatas in this collection, performed by pianist Diane Hidy (GP391CD). Ms. Hidy's interpretations are closely matched to this edition as a practical example for students.

ISBN 0-8497-6200-6

DOMENICO SCARLATTI (1685-1757)

Domenico Scarlatti was born in Naples, Italy in 1685. His father, Allesandro Scarlatti, was a famous musician and composer throughout Europe. At the age of 16, Scarlatti became the organist and composer for the Royal Chapel in Naples, where his father was the maestro di capella (choir director). In 1708, Scarlatti moved to Rome. Here he was in service to the Queen Maria Casimira of Poland and eventually became maestro di capella of the Vatican. During his years in Rome, Scarlatti met and became friends with the composer George Friedrich Handel (1685-1759). In 1724, Scarlatti moved to Lisbon. Here he was music teacher of the daughter of King John V of Portugal, Maria Barbara. In 1728, Maria Barbara married the Spanish Crown Prince Fernando and moved to Madrid. Scarlatti accompanied her and remained in Madrid for the rest of his life. Scarlatti became so closely associated with Spain that his name eventually appeared as Domingo Escarlatti. From 1752- 1756, Scarlatti was the teacher of Spanish composer Antonio Soler (1729-1783). Scarlatti died in Madrid in 1757.

Scarlatti held a reputation as the finest harpsichord player of his day. It is said that when judged next to Handel, Scarlatti was the better on the harpsichord but Handel superior on the organ. (The two famous composers held each other in highest esteem both as musicians and friends throughout their lives.) It could be said that Scarlatti was the "father of the virtuoso performer." His style of composition showed a great departure from the strict contrapuntal rules of the era. Homophonic in texture and generally in binary form, his keyboard writing introduced many new opportunities for technical display, including rapid scales in thirds and sixths, repeated notes played by quickly changing fingers, and many crossed hand passages.

Scarlatti wrote between 500-600 Sonatas during his years in Madrid. It is generally assumed that these works are written expressly for the harpsichord. However, it is notable that Maria Barbara had two pianos, and, since many of the sonatas were written for her, it is reasonable that at least some are intended for the piano.

Very few of Scarlatti's keyboard sonatas were published during his lifetime. In 1839, renowned piano pedagogue Carl Czerny (1791-1857) collected and published 200 sonatas in Vienna. Piano virtuoso Franz Liszt (1811-1886) campaigned for renewed interest in the sonatas in the late 19th century. Eventually, the virtually complete edition by A. Longo (1864-1945)–including 545 sonatas in 11 volumes–was published in 1906.

ABOUT THIS EDITION

This volume contains ten sonatas selected by the editor. The sonatas are placed in order of difficulty. Fingering, dynamics, slurs, and staccatos are added by the editor as suggestions for musical interpretation.

The painting on the cover of this book is by William Claesz Heda (1599-1680/82) and is titled *Breakfast Still Life with Roemer* (1640). Heda painted Dutch still life and is known as one of the best painters of this genre.

SONATA IN D MINOR

L. 423

SONATA IN A MAJOR

L. 483

6

7

GP391

SONATA IN G MAJOR

L. 79

Sonata in D Minor

L. 58

SONATA IN D MAJOR

L. 463

Non presto, ma a tempo di ballo

© 1996 Neil A. Kjos Music Company, 4380 Jutland Drive, San Diego, California 92117.

14

GP391

SONATA IN E MAJOR

L. 23

Andante tranquillo

SONATA IN C MAJOR

L. 104

SONATA IN D MINOR
L. 422

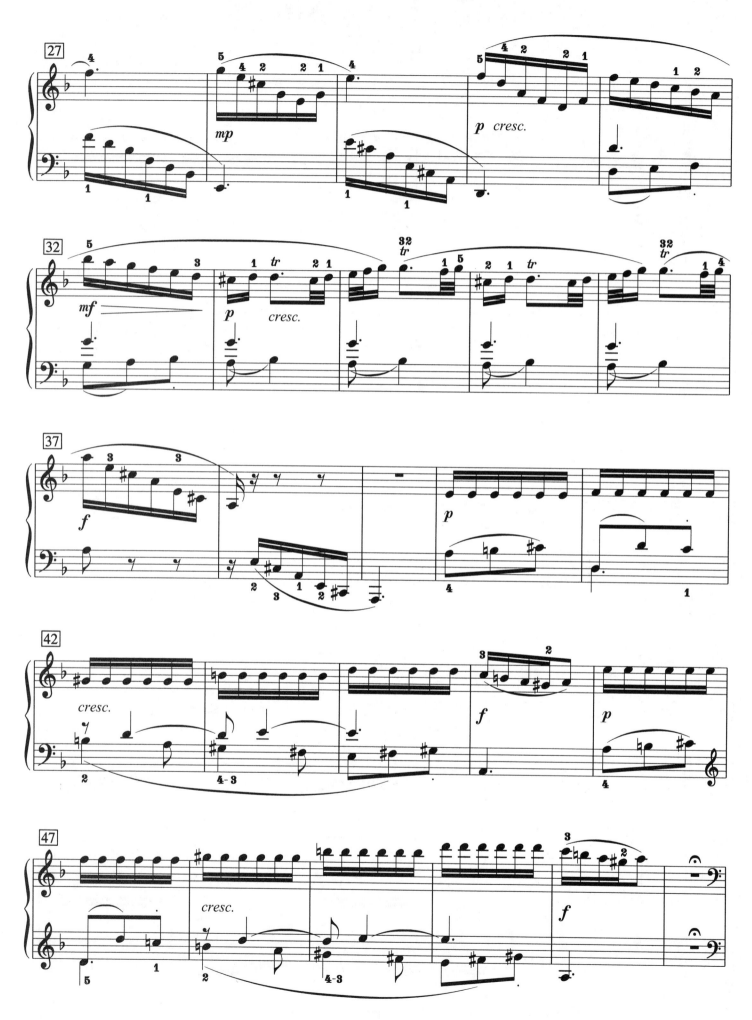

26

GP391

SONATA IN A MAJOR

L. 345

32

GP391

34

GP391

Sonata in D major
L. 461